Contents

Written by
Jon Blake

Illustrated by
Paul Williams

Series editor **Dee Reid**

ALWAYS LEA... ...RSON

Before reading Star for a Day

Characters

Calum

Rose

Jordan York

Nell

A scary fan

New vocabulary

ch1 p5 manager

ch2 p9 makeover

ch2 p9 noticing

ch2 p11 staring

ch3 p13 zombie

ch3 p15 ignore

Introduction

Calum looks just like teen superstar Jordan York. When Calum's friend, Rose, puts his picture on the Jordan York fan page, Calum is contacted by Jordan York's manager who thinks Calum will be just right for a job she has in mind.

Star for a Day

Chapter One

"Hey, Calum, look at this," said Rose. Calum looked at the picture in the magazine Rose was reading. It was a picture of Jordan York. The magazine said Jordan would be the biggest teen superstar in the world.

"Does he remind you of anyone?" asked Rose.

"Yes," said Calum slowly. "He looks just like me!"

"We should put your photo on the Jordan York fan page on Facebook," said Rose.

"No way!" said Calum.

But when Rose got an idea in her head there was no stopping her. In two days, Calum had three hundred new friends. In a week, he had three thousand friends.

Then Calum got a message:

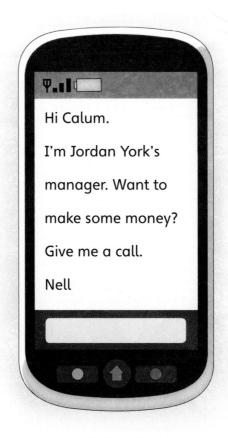

Hi Calum.

I'm Jordan York's

manager. Want to

make some money?

Give me a call.

Nell

"Someone's playing a joke on me," said Calum.

"There's only one way to find out," said Rose.

Calum rang the number and it really was Jordan York's manager, Nell.

"Jordan is doing a TV show in your town," she said. "We need someone who can pretend to be Jordan to keep the fans away from him. We'll pay you £1000."

Wow! thought Calum, *£1000 for one day's work!*

"OK," he said.

Chapter Two

The next Saturday, Calum was in a smart hotel in town waiting for the teen pop idol.

When Jordan saw Calum he couldn't believe it.

"It's just like looking in a mirror!" he said.

"Thanks for coming here today," said Jordan. "I love my fans but some of them are just crazy. They know things about me I don't know myself!"

Calum could hear Jordan's fans. There were hundreds of them shouting and screaming outside the hotel.

"Time for your makeover Calum," said Nell.

When Calum was ready, it was his job to stand at the window and pretend to be Jordan so that the real Jordan could sneak out of the hotel without the fans noticing.

Jordan left and Calum went over to the window.

All the fans screamed.

Cool! thought Calum. Calum waved and heard

more screaming. *This is fun*, thought Calum.

Then Calum noticed a boy in the crowd. He wasn't waving and screaming like the rest of the fans. He just stood deadly still, staring at Calum.

He looks really scary, thought Calum.

Chapter Three

Nell had told Calum to go to the window every twenty minutes. Every time he went, the scary boy was still staring. Then it began to pour with rain. *That'll get rid of him*, thought Calum.

When Calum went to the window again,

all the fans had gone except for the boy.

He was soaked but he was still staring at

Calum like a zombie.

It was dark outside when Jordan York came back.

"Did you enjoy being me?" he asked Calum.

"Not really," replied Calum.

"Why not?" asked Jordan.

"There's this guy down there," said Calum. "He's just been staring at me all day."

"Oh, there are always nutters," replied Jordan. "I ignore them."

It was alright for Jordan to say that. He had minders to look after him. Calum didn't have minders and he had to get home.

"We'll get you a taxi," said Nell.

"Thanks," said Calum.

When Calum had changed back into his own clothes, Nell counted out his wages, all in new notes. It was the most money Calum had ever seen in his life. But when Calum thought about the nutter waiting for him outside the hotel he felt a chill run down his spine.

Chapter Four

Calum went into the bathroom to wet his hair and comb it into a style that was nothing like Jordan's. But he couldn't change his face. He still looked just like Jordan York.

As Calum left the hotel he put his head down and ran for the taxi.

But then he heard someone running after him calling, "Jordan! Wait! I'm your number one fan!"

Calum looked back. He was staring into the face of the scary boy. "They made me pretend to be Jordan York!" explained Calum. "I'm not him!"

The boy had a crazy look on his face. He grabbed Calum's arm. "Of course you're Jordan York. I've been waiting all day to meet you!" Calum tried to pull away from the boy but the boy just gripped even harder.

"You're making a mistake," shouted Calum, looking around for help.

Just then, a white limo shot past. The number plate was FAME 1. In the back seat Jordan York was talking on his mobile.

The boy looked from the limo to Calum. Then
he gave Calum a hard shove and began running
down the street after the limo calling, "Jordan!
Wait! I'm your number one fan!"

Better to look like Jordan York than to be him,
thought Calum as he climbed into the taxi, patting
the £1000 in his pocket.

Quiz

Text comprehension

Literal comprehension

p4 How did Jordan York's manager get to know about Calum?

p14 Why did Calum not enjoy being Jordan York?

p17 What does Calum do to avoid looking like Jordan York?

Inferential comprehension

p18 Why do you think the scary boy was so sure that Calum was Jordan York?

p20 Why do you think the scary boy gave Calum a shove?

p20 Why does Calum think it is better to look like Jordan York than to be him?

Personal response

- Would you like to be a lookalike for a superstar? If so, which superstar?
- Do you think £1000 was worth it for the stress of pretending to be Jordan York?
- Why might some people become crazy fans?

Author's style

p13 What simile does the author use to describe the scary boy?

p16 What description does the author use to explain that Calum felt scared?

p20 Why does the author tell us that Calum pats the £1000 in his pocket?

Characters

- Calum
- **Jordan** (teen superstar)
- **Nell** (Jordan's manager)
- **Joe** (Jordan's bodyguard)

Setting the scene

Calum has been a lookalike for Jordan York all day. It's not all been fun because he has been bothered by one fan who has spent the whole day just staring at him through the hotel window. Then Jordan, his manager and his bodyguard arrive back at the hotel.

Jordan: Result! That worked really well.

Nell: Yes, our plan to fool the fans worked like a dream.

Jordan: We didn't see any fans all day.

Joe: I didn't have to get rid of any fans at all. There was nothing for me to do!

Calum: It's great that the plan worked.

Jordan: Did you like pretending to be me, Calum?

Nell: Yes, what did you think of being a superstar for the day?

Calum: It wasn't as much fun as I thought it was going to be.

Jordan: How can you say that? My life is great!

Calum: I think the crowd of crazy fans just stressed me out.

Nell: That's a shame. We were hoping that you would pretend to be Jordan next weekend as well.

Jordan: Because my normal lookalike is out of action.

Calum: What do you mean? Why is your normal lookalike out of action?

Joe: Didn't Nell tell you? Jordan's normal lookalike has got a broken wrist.

Nell: There's no need to bother Calum with all that.

Calum: Why? What happened to him?

Jordan: He was mobbed by fans. They knocked him over and he broke his wrist. It's no big deal.

Nell: So are you on for next weekend or not, Calum?

Calum: Sorry. I don't want to be Jordan's lookalike next weekend. It really freaked me out.

Jordan: How can you be freaked out by pretending to be me?

Calum: There's a crazy guy outside the hotel.

Nell: Why is he freaking you out Calum?

Calum: He's been there all day, just staring at me. He hasn't moved, not even when it started pouring with rain.

Joe: Tell me about it. There are plenty of crazy fans out there.

Jordan: That's why I've got Joe. He looks after me and makes sure I don't get mobbed by the fans!

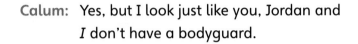

Calum: Yes, but I look just like you, Jordan and *I* don't have a bodyguard.

Nell: Don't worry Calum. I'll get you a taxi and I'll get it to wait just outside the hotel.

Jordan: I have to get ready for my film premiere tonight. See you, Calum. Shame you can't make next weekend.

Nell: Here's your money. I'm sure there is nothing to worry about. See you.

Calum: Can Joe go with me to the taxi?

Joe: Sorry, Calum. I'm not paid to look after you. You're on your own.

Quiz

Text comprehension

p24 Why is Nell disappointed that Calum didn't much enjoy being Jordan's lookalike?

p25 Why does Nell not want Joe to talk about what happened to the normal lookalike?

p27 Why is Jordan not bothered about crazy fans?

Vocabulary

p25 Find a word meaning 'usual'.

p26 Find a phrase meaning 'made me panic'.

p27 Find a phrase meaning 'very wet weather'.

Before reading DOUBLES

Find out about

- why some people use doubles or lookalikes.

New vocabulary

p32 trained
p32 pretending
p36 episode

p36 noticed
p37 celebrity
p38 competition

Introduction

Some people use a double so that if someone wanted to kill them, they wouldn't know who was the double and who was the real person! Some film actors use doubles for dangerous scenes but some do their own stunts. Some lookalikes make a lot of money just by pretending to be someone else!

DOUBLES

Do you think there is someone in the world who looks just like you? There are over 7 billion people in the world, so it's a fair bet that one of them looks like you. When someone looks like another person, we call them a *lookalike* or a *double*.

Doubles

Some powerful people use a double so that if someone wanted to kill them they wouldn't know who was the double and who was the real person. These doubles are trained to speak and walk like the person they are pretending to be. They might even have plastic surgery to make them look more like the real person.

Adolf Hitler had a double who looked just like him. His double was called Julius Schreck. Look at the photos below.

Can you tell who is Adolf Hitler?

Stunt Doubles

Film actors often have stunt doubles who look just like them. When the action in the film is dangerous, the stunt double takes over. Even if you look at the film very closely you will not be able to tell if you are looking at the actor or the double.

Some actors are famous for performing their own stunts instead of using stunt doubles. So even if the action in the film is very dangerous, the actor performs the stunt.

Animal Doubles

The first pet on 'Blue Peter' was a dog called Petra. Sadly, Petra died after one episode. The Blue Peter team found a lookalike for Petra. They didn't tell viewers what had happened to Petra and none of the viewers noticed that it was not the same dog as in the first episode.

In the 'Harry Potter' films the dog, Fang, is played by four different dogs but most viewers think it is just one dog.

Celebrity Lookalikes

Nowadays, most pop singers and actors have a lookalike. The lookalikes appear at events and parties and make lots of money by pretending to be someone else! People know it's not the real celebrity but they still like to see them. It's not just pop singers and actors who have lookalikes. Even members of the royal family have lookalikes!

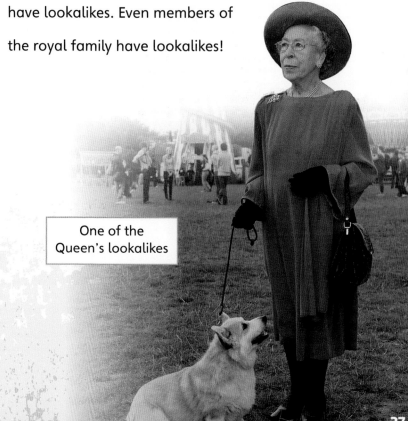

One of the Queen's lookalikes

However, celebrity lookalikes are nothing new. In 1915, there was a competition to find the best lookalike for Charlie Chaplin. The real Charlie Chaplin secretly entered the competition but he didn't even make the final! The judges didn't think he looked like Charlie Chaplin!

Quiz

Text comprehension

Literal comprehension
p31 Why is there a chance that there is someone in the world who looks just like you?

p32–33 Why would Adolf Hitler want a double?

p36 Why didn't viewers notice that it was a different Petra?

Inferential comprehension
p35 Why do you think some actors like to do their own dangerous stunts?

p36 Why do you think the Blue Peter team did not want to tell viewers about the death of the first Petra?

p37 Why do you think people want to see lookalikes?

Personal response
- How would you make good use of a double if you had one?
- Do you think it is cheating if an actor uses a double?
- Would you go to see a lookalike?

Non-fiction features

p32 Think of a caption for this picture.

p36 Think of a subheading for the second paragraph.

p38 Think of a heading for this page.

Published by Pearson Education Limited, Edinburgh Gate, Harlow, Essex, CM20 2JE.

www.pearsonschoolsandfecolleges.co.uk

Text © Pearson Education Limited 2012

Edited by Jo Dilloway
Designed by Tony Richardson and Siu Hang Wong
Original illustrations © Pearson Education Limited 2012
Illustrated by Paul Williams
Cover design by Siu Hang Wong
Picture research by Melissa Allison

Cover illustration © Pearson Education Limited 2012

The right of Jon Blake to be identified as author of this work has been asserted by him in accordance with the Copyright, Designs and Patents Act 1988.

First published 2012

16 15 14 13 12
10 9 8 7 6 5 4 3 2 1

British Library Cataloguing in Publication Data
A catalogue record for this book is available from the British Library

ISBN 978 0 435 07099 1

Printed at Scotprint, UK.

Acknowledgements
The author and publisher would like to thank the following individuals and organisations for permission to reproduce photographs:

(Key: b-bottom; c-centre; l-left; r-right; t-top)

Getty Images: Gamma-Rapho 36, Hulton Archive 33r, Ian Gavan 37, Moviepix 38, Stone+ 31; Press Association Images: AP 32, 33l; Shutterstock.com: PhotoStock10 1, 34-35

Cover images: Back: Getty Images: Ian Gavan

All other images © Pearson Education

Every effort has been made to contact copyright holders of material reproduced in this book. Any omissions will be rectified in subsequent printings if notice is given to the publishers.